IQ
Interactive
Puzzles

Managing Editors: Simon Melhuish and Sarah Wells
Series Editor: Nikole G Bamford
Designer: Linley J Clode
Writer: Philip Carter
Illustrator: Linley J Clode

Published by
The Lagoon Group
PO Box 311, KT2 5QW, UK
PO Box 990676, Boston, MA 02199, USA

ISBN: 1904797024

www.thelagoongroup.com

Printed in China

IQ
Interactive
Puzzles

IntelliQuest

UNIQUE BOOK CODE	010

Instructions

First of all make sure you have a Quizmo —

Find the book's unique code (this appears at the top of this page). Use the ◄ and ► buttons to scroll to this number on the Quizmo screen. Press the ↵ button to enter the code, and you're ready to go.

Use the ◄ ► scroll buttons to select the question number you want to answer. Press the Ⓐ, Ⓑ, Ⓒ, or Ⓓ button to enter your chosen answer.

If you are correct the green light beside the button you pressed will flash. You can then use the scroll button to move on to another question.

If your answer is incorrect, the red light beside the button you pressed will flash.

Don't worry, you can try again and again until you have the correct answer, OR move on to another question. (Beware: the more times you guess incorrectly, the lower your final percentage score will be!)

You can finish the quiz at any point — just press the 🔷 button to find out your score and rank as follows:

75% or above	Wow! You're a genius!
50% — 74%	You're one bright spark!
25% — 49%	Oh dear, time to fill up your think tank...
Less than 25%	Emergency! You've got a serious case of brain drain!

If you do press the 🔷 button to find out your score, this will end your session and you will have to use the 🔷 to start again!

HAVE FUN!

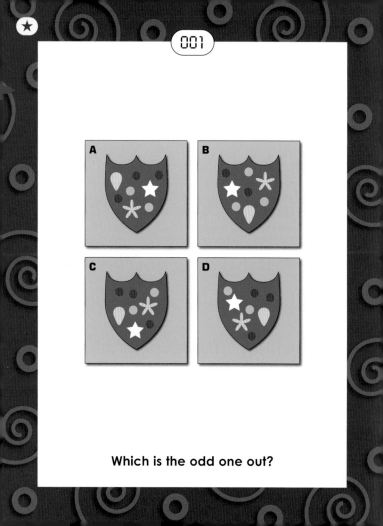

Which is the odd one out?

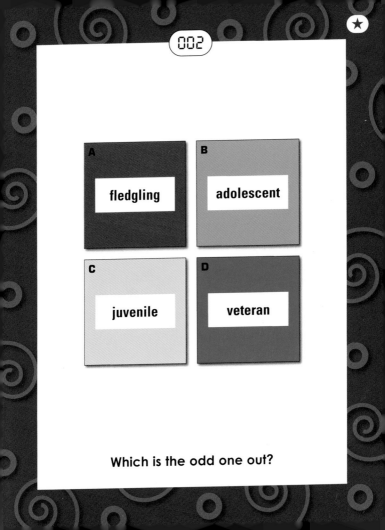

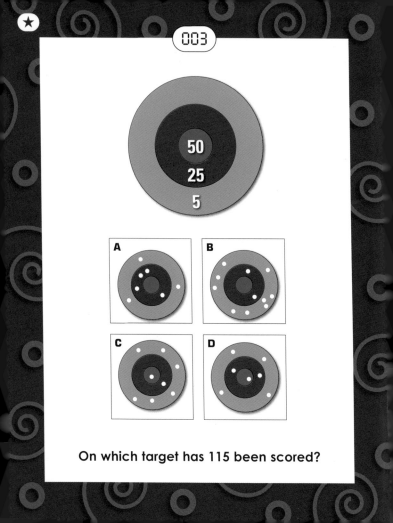

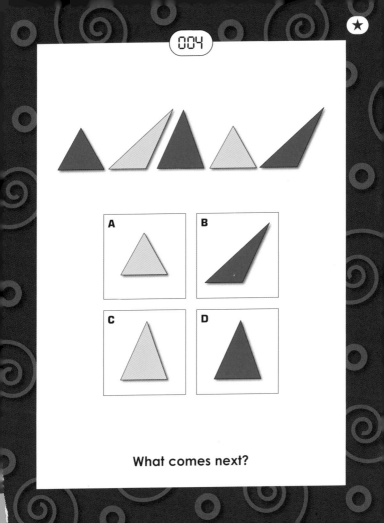

A

B

C

D

What comes next?

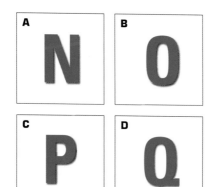

005

ACFJ?

A N

B O

C P

D Q

What comes next?

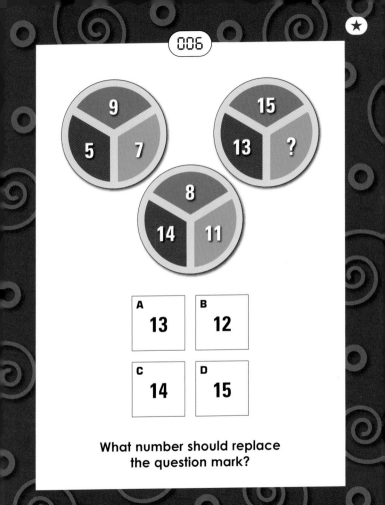

What number should replace
the question mark?

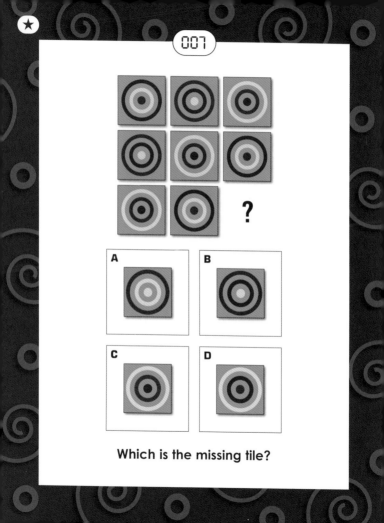

Which is the missing tile?

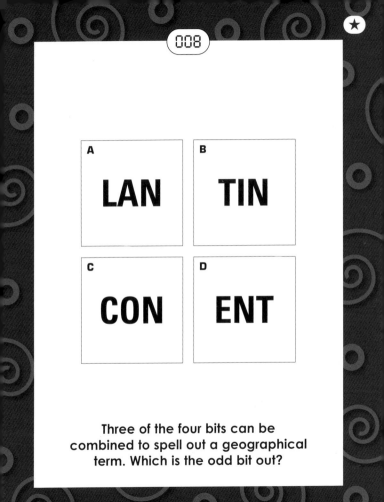

A

LAN

B

TIN

C

CON

D

ENT

Three of the four bits can be combined to spell out a geographical term. Which is the odd bit out?

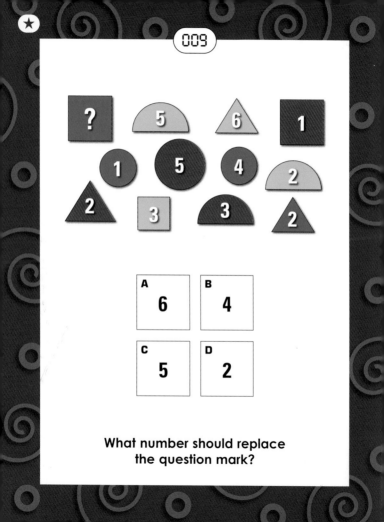

What number should replace
the question mark?

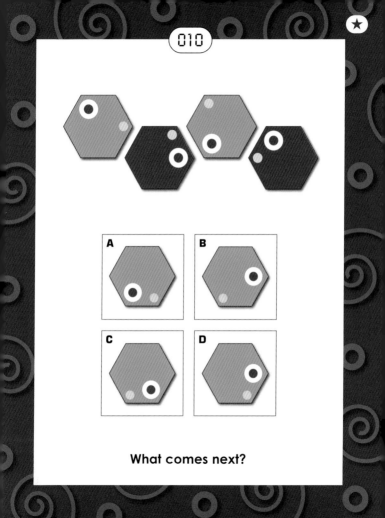

What comes next?

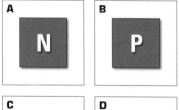

A N

B P

C O

D Q

Which is the missing letter?

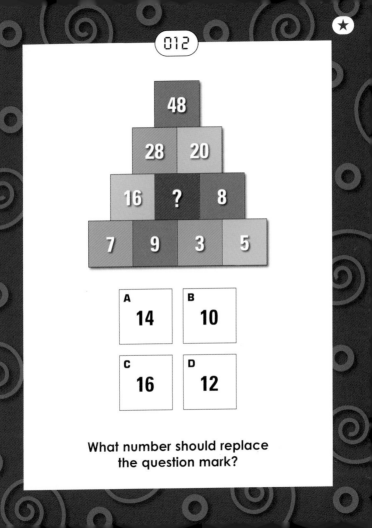

012

48

28 20

16 ? 8

7 9 3 5

A 14

B 10

C 16

D 12

What number should replace
the question mark?

Which is the odd one out?

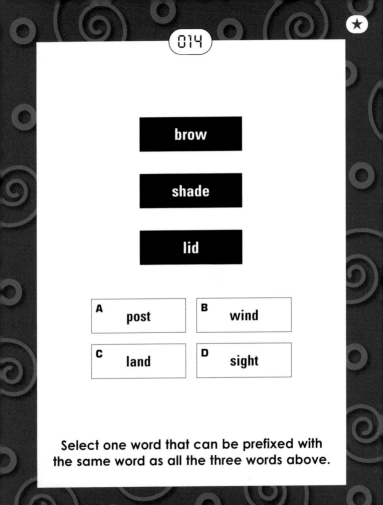

014

brow

shade

lid

A post

B wind

C land

D sight

Select one word that can be prefixed with the same word as all the three words above.

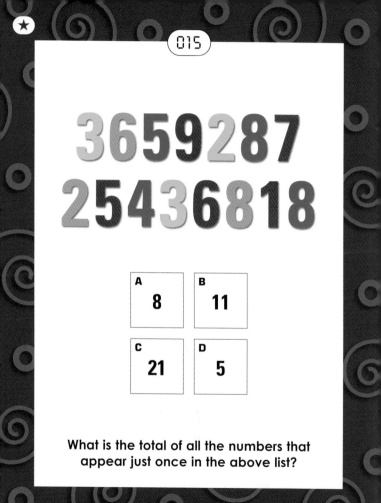

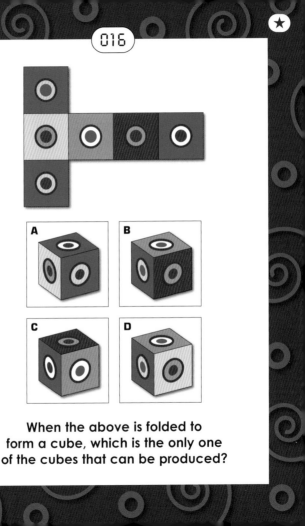

When the above is folded to form a cube, which is the only one of the cubes that can be produced?

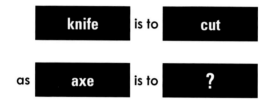

knife is to **cut**

as **axe** is to **?**

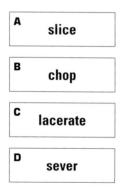

A	slice
B	chop
C	lacerate
D	sever

1, 1, 2.5, 3.5, 4, 6, 5.5, ?

A	B
7	8.5

C	D
7.5	9

What number comes next?

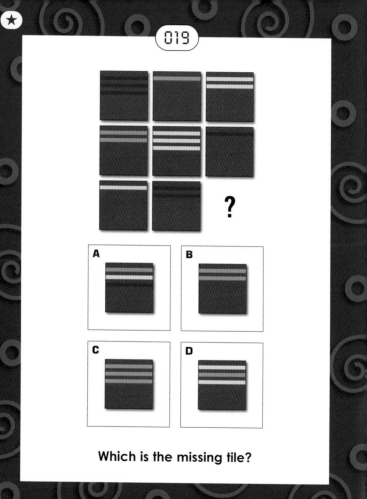

019

?

A

B

C

D

Which is the missing tile?

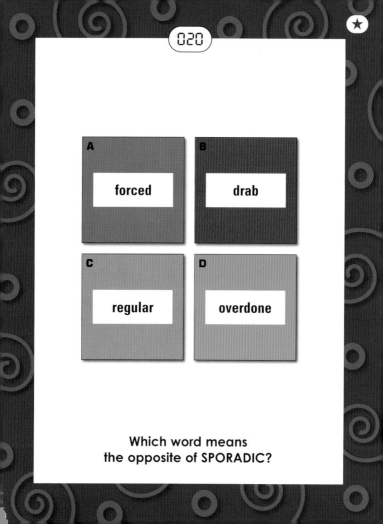

A forced

B drab

C regular

D overdone

Which word means
the opposite of SPORADIC?

A **$468.00**

B **$441.00**

C **$450.00**

D **$432.00**

Jack and Jill share a certain
amount of money in the ratio 4:5. If Jill
has $240.00, how much is shared?

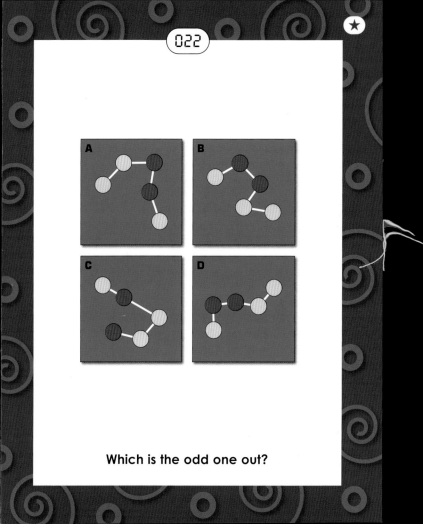

Which is the odd one out?

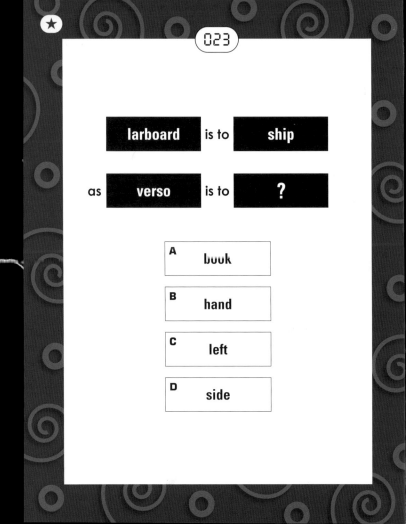

larboard is to **ship**

as **verso** is to **?**

A **book**

B **hand**

C **left**

D **side**

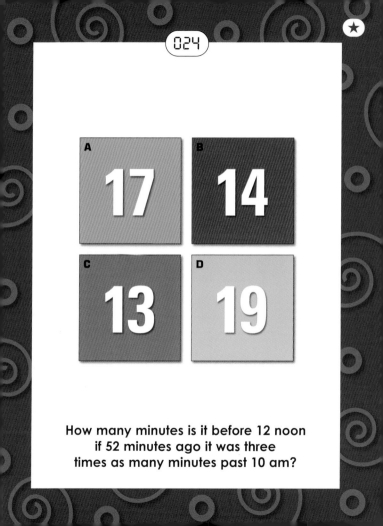

A 17

B 14

C 13

D 19

How many minutes is it before 12 noon
if 52 minutes ago it was three
times as many minutes past 10 am?

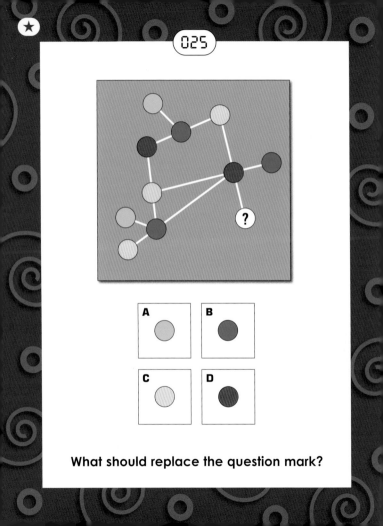

A

B

C

D

What should replace the question mark?

A

GTHMI

B

KICEN

C

DINEC

D

APHTE

Which is the only group of five
letters above that can be rearranged to
spell out a 5-letter English word?

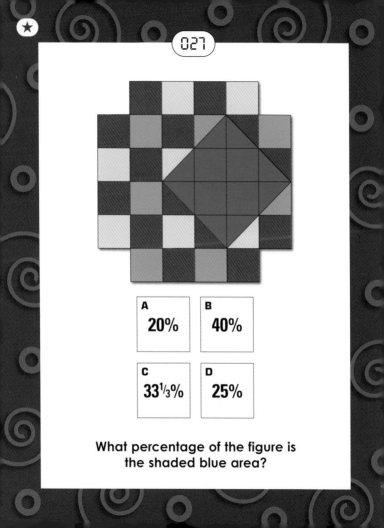

A
20%

B
40%

C
33⅓%

D
25%

What percentage of the figure is
the shaded blue area?

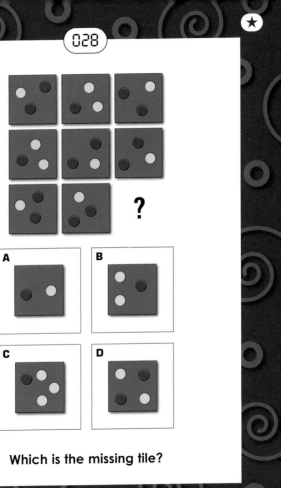

Which is the missing tile?

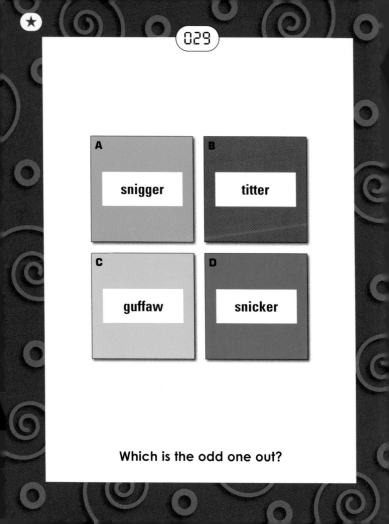

029

A snigger

B titter

C guffaw

D snicker

Which is the odd one out?

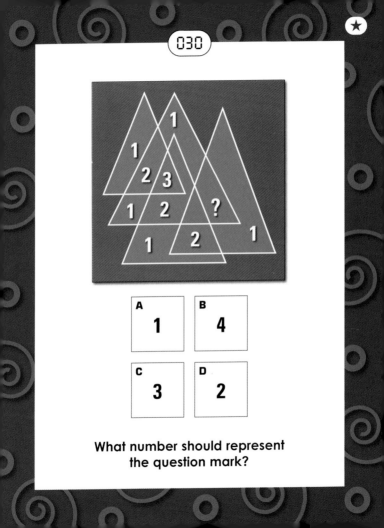

A 1

B 4

C 3

D 2

What number should represent the question mark?

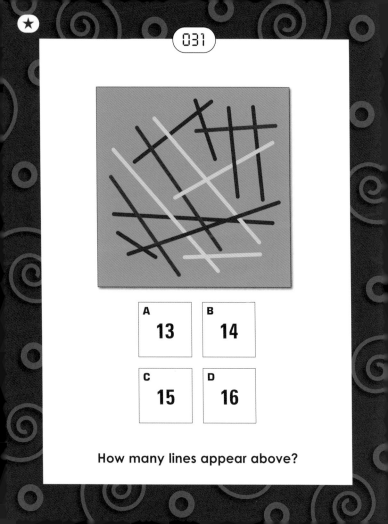

A 13

B 14

C 15

D 16

How many lines appear above?

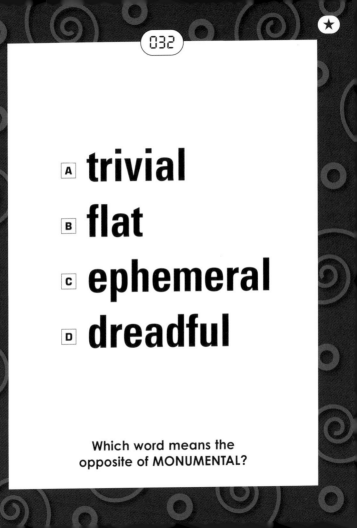

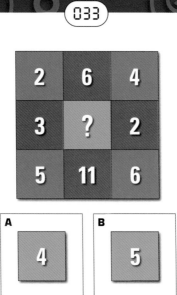

033

2	6	4
3	?	2
5	11	6

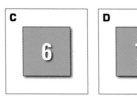

A

4

B

5

C

6

D

7

What number should replace
the question mark?

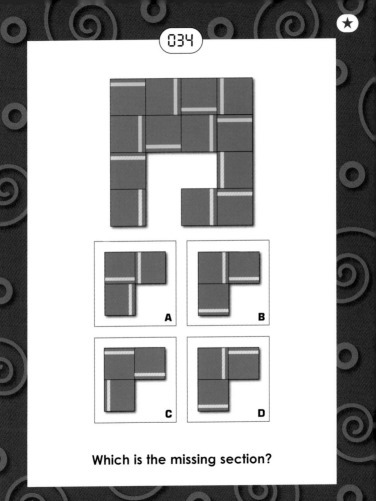

034

A

B

C

D

Which is the missing section?

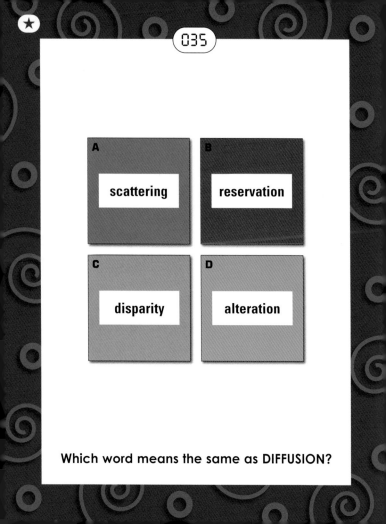

A scattering

B reservation

C disparity

D alteration

Which word means the same as DIFFUSION?

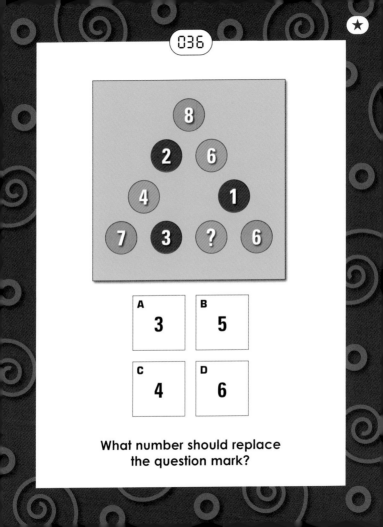

A 3

B 5

C 4

D 6

What number should replace
the question mark?

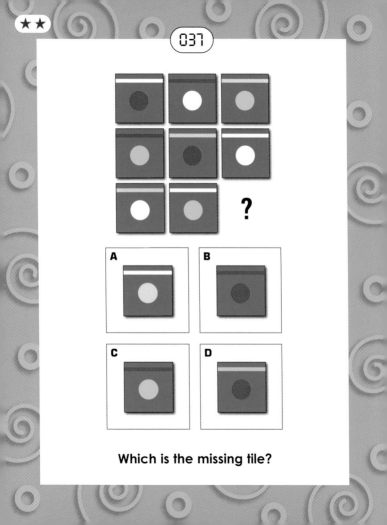

Which is the missing tile?

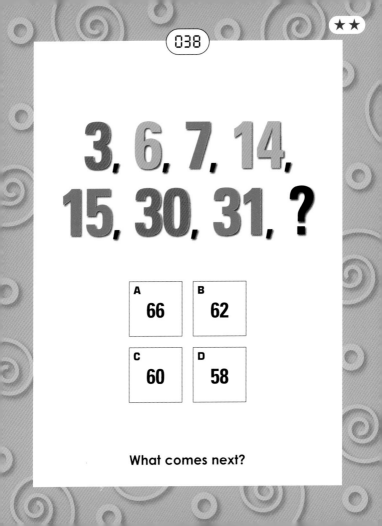

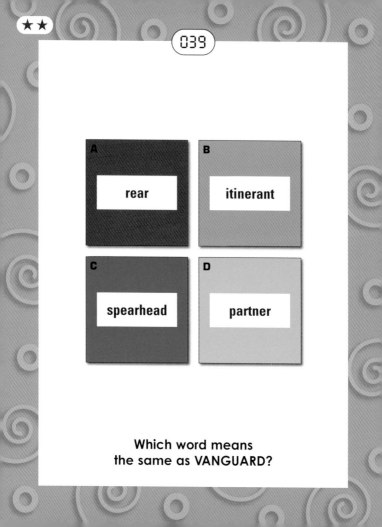

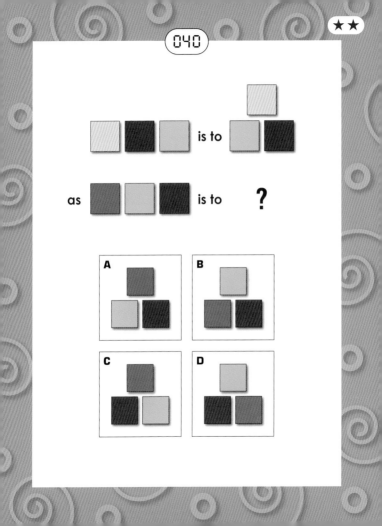

A **tibia**

B **ulna**

C **radius**

D **humerus**

Which is the odd one out?

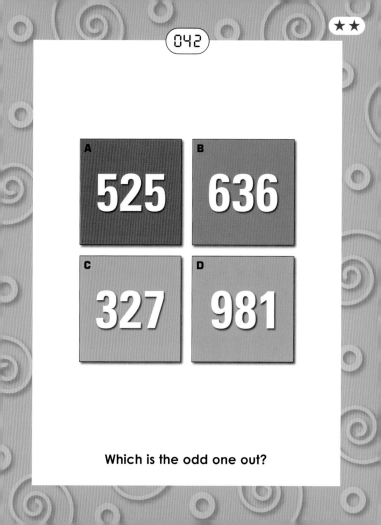

A 525

B 636

C 327

D 981

Which is the odd one out?

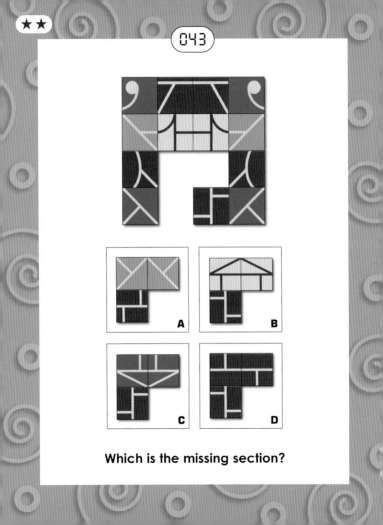

043

Which is the missing section?

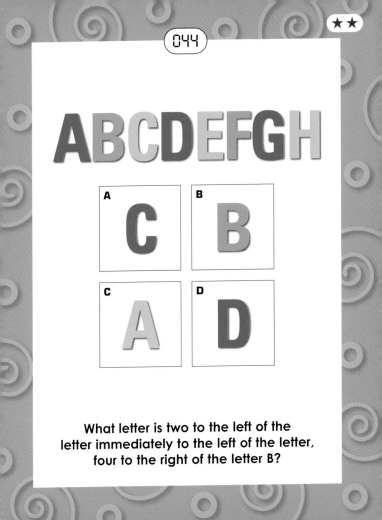

100, 96.5, 97.25, 93.75, 94.5, ?

A 91

B 91.75

C 90.75

D 91.5

What comes next?

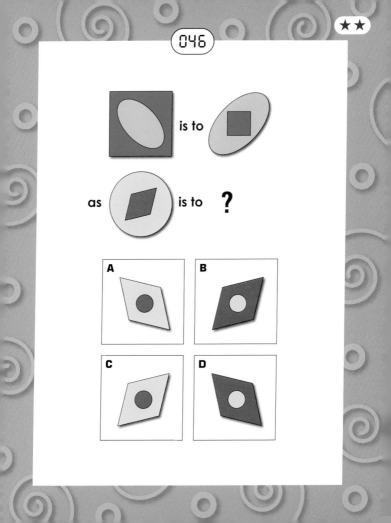

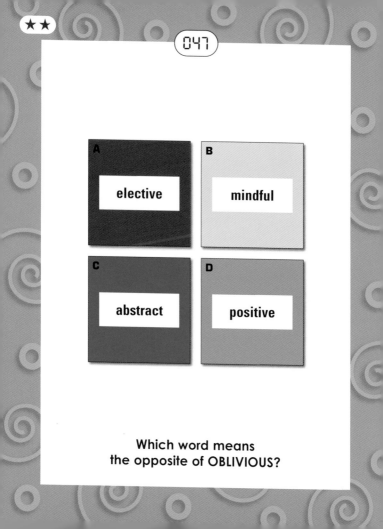

A **elective**

B **mindful**

C **abstract**

D **positive**

Which word means
the opposite of OBLIVIOUS?

38472 is to 74283

and

59731 is to 37195

therefore

68143 is to ?

A 43168

B 14386

C 41368

D 41386

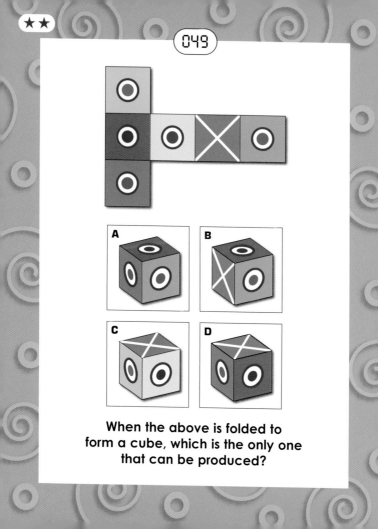

When the above is folded to
form a cube, which is the only one
that can be produced?

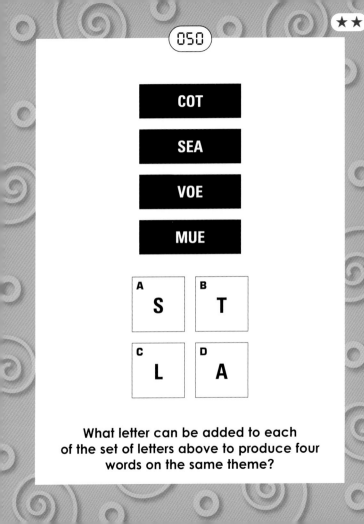

COT

SEA

VOE

MUE

A S

B T

C L

D A

What letter can be added to each
of the set of letters above to produce four
words on the same theme?

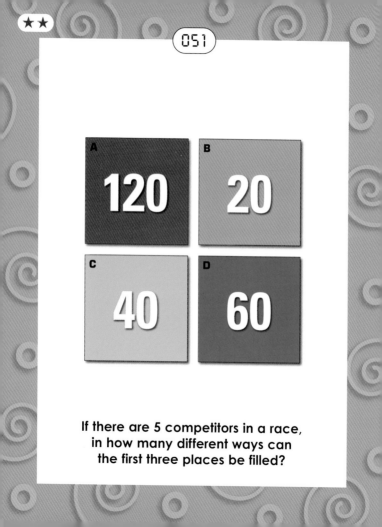

051

A 120

B 20

C 40

D 60

If there are 5 competitors in a race, in how many different ways can the first three places be filled?

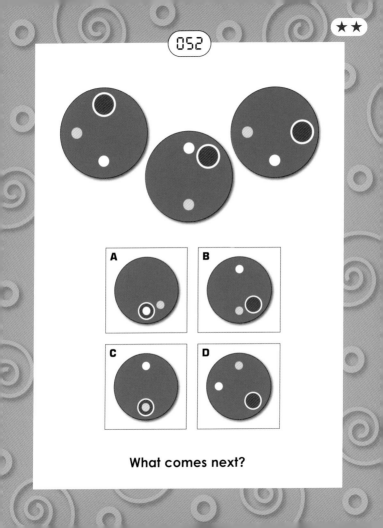

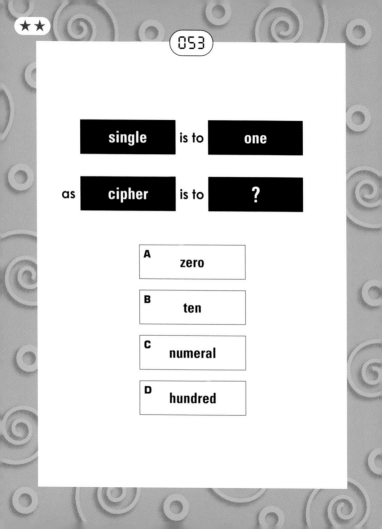

single is to one

as cipher is to ?

A zero

B ten

C numeral

D hundred

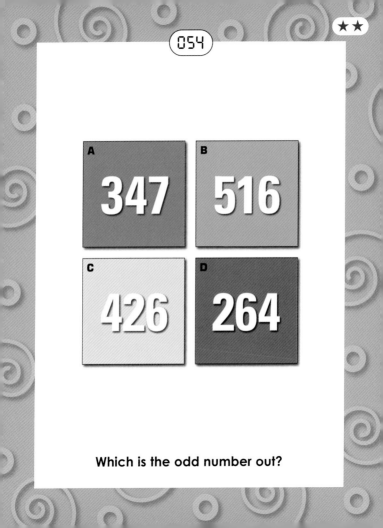

A 347

B 516

C 426

D 264

Which is the odd number out?

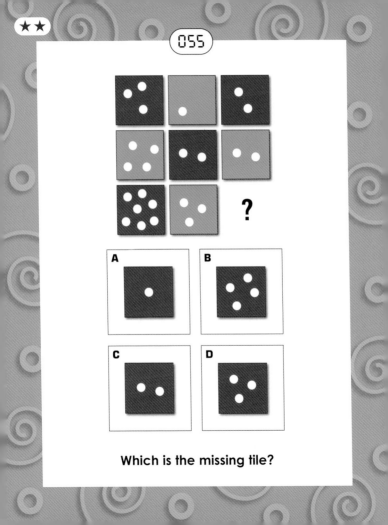

Which is the missing tile?

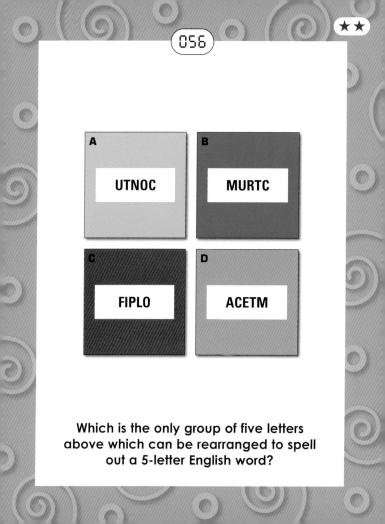

A UTNOC

B MURTC

C FIPLO

D ACETM

Which is the only group of five letters above which can be rearranged to spell out a 5-letter English word?

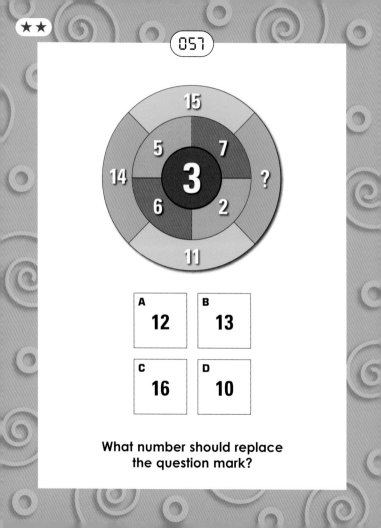

What number should replace
the question mark?

When the above is folded to
form a cube, which is the only one
that can be produced?

★★

3	6	3	12
2	1	7	3
6	3	9	7
4	8	6	?

A 8

B 6

C 10

D 14

What number should replace
the question mark?

chemistry is to **substances**

as **fauna** is to **?**

A plants

B forests

C environment

D animals

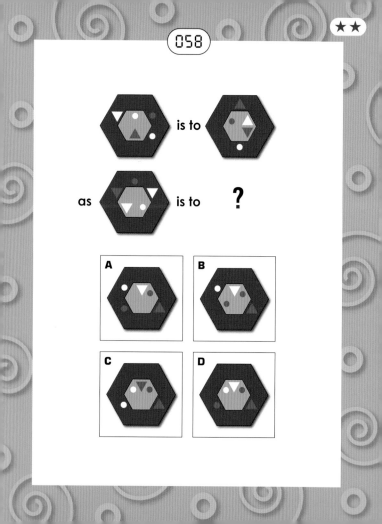

★★

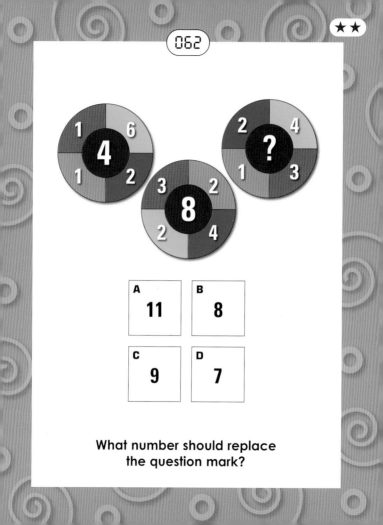

A
11

B
8

C
9

D
7

What number should replace
the question mark?

stet is to **reinstate**

as **caret** is to **?**

A insert

B gold

C mark

D delete

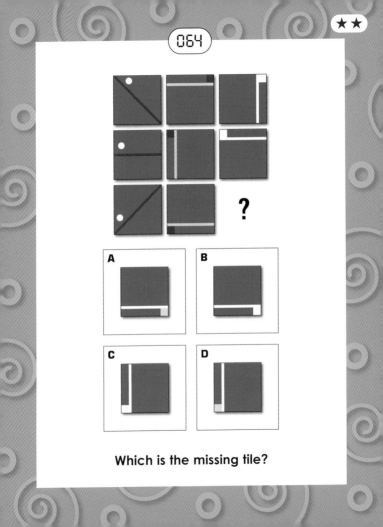

Which is the missing tile?

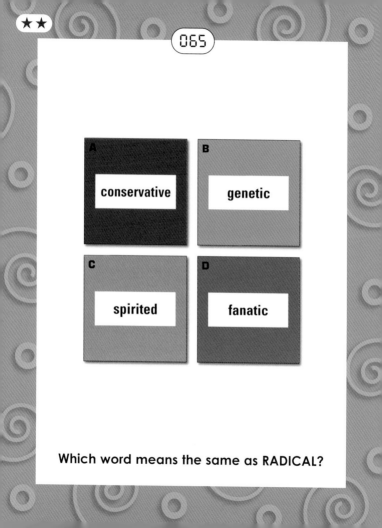

A **conservative**

B **genetic**

C **spirited**

D **fanatic**

Which word means the same as RADICAL?

3	5	8	10
6	8	11	13
8	10	13	15
11	13	16	?

A 17

B 19

C 18

D 21

What number should replace
the question mark?

A

B

C

D

To which shield can a dot be
added so that it meets the same
conditions as in the shield above?

1, 7, 8, 15, 23 ?

A
30

B
38

C
35

D
41

What comes next?

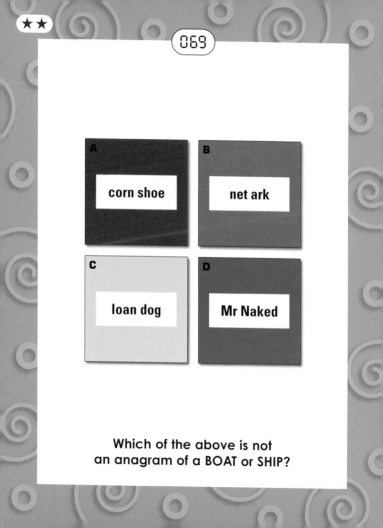

★★

069

A corn shoe

B net ark

C loan dog

D Mr Naked

Which of the above is not
an anagram of a BOAT or SHIP?

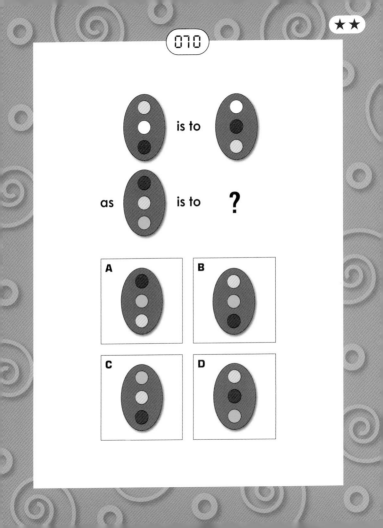

A accost

B snub

C insult

D destroy

Which word means the opposite of HAIL?

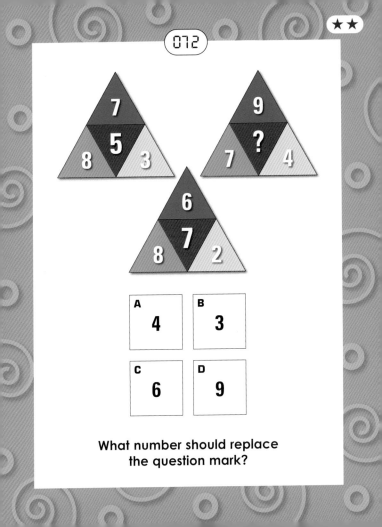

072

What number should replace
the question mark?

A   4

B   3

C   6

D   9

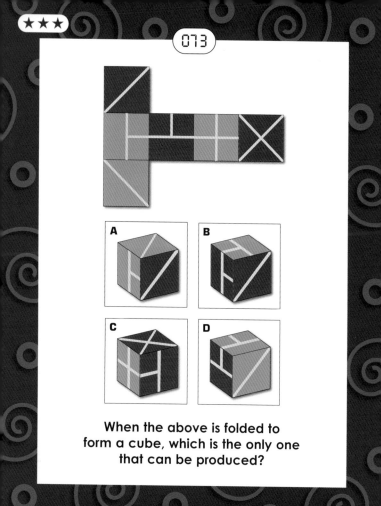

When the above is folded to form a cube, which is the only one that can be produced?

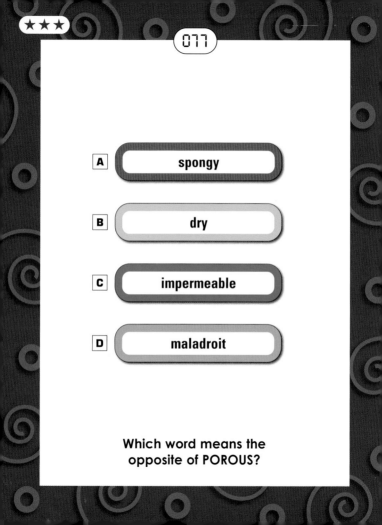

A spongy

B dry

C impermeable

D maladroit

Which word means the
opposite of POROUS?

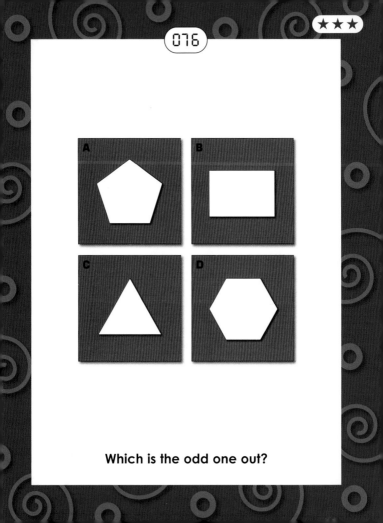

Which is the odd one out?

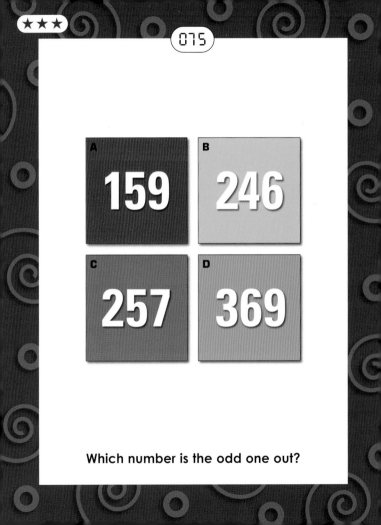

A
159

B
246

C
257

D
369

Which number is the odd one out?

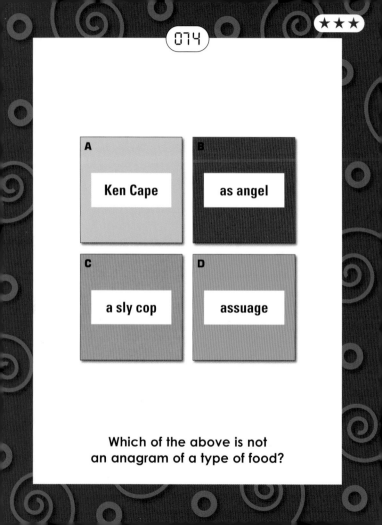

A

Ken Cape

B

as angel

C

a sly cop

D

assuage

Which of the above is not
an anagram of a type of food?

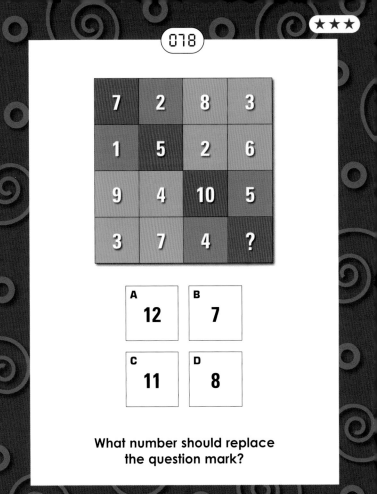

A 12

B 7

C 11

D 8

What number should replace
the question mark?

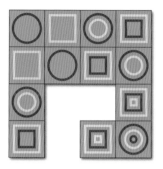

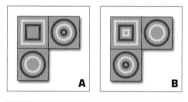

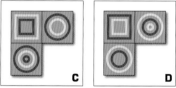

Which is the missing section?

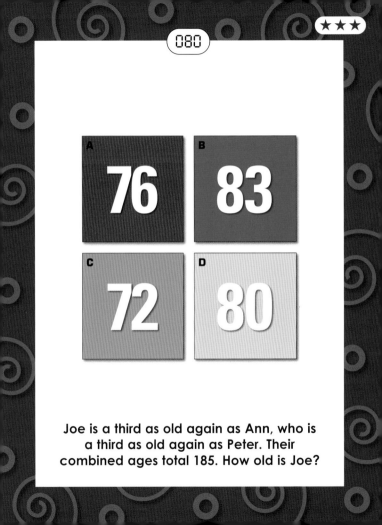

A **76**

B **83**

C **72**

D **80**

Joe is a third as old again as Ann, who is a third as old again as Peter. Their combined ages total 185. How old is Joe?

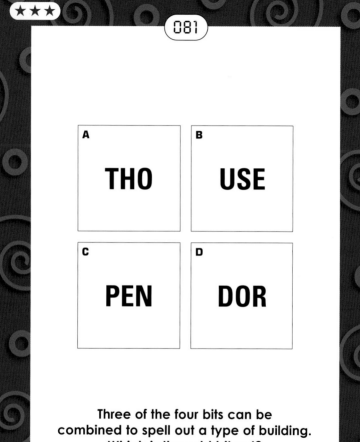

A

THO

B

USE

C

PEN

D

DOR

Three of the four bits can be
combined to spell out a type of building.
Which is the odd bit out?

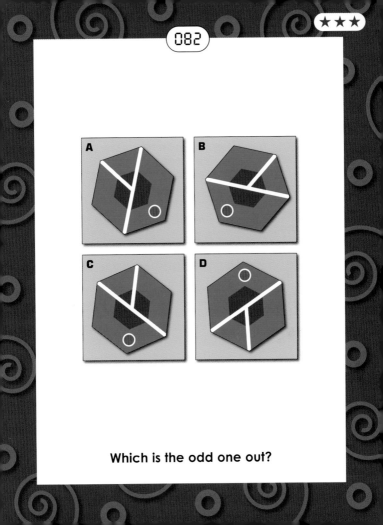

★★★

Which is the odd one out?

A	smooth
B	swift
C	mistaken
D	knowledgeable

Which word means the same as ERUDITE?

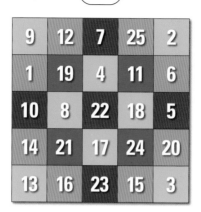

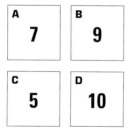

A 7

B 9

C 5

D 10

What number is two places away from itself plus 2, three places away from itself plus 3, one place away from itself plus 1, and two places away from itself less 2?

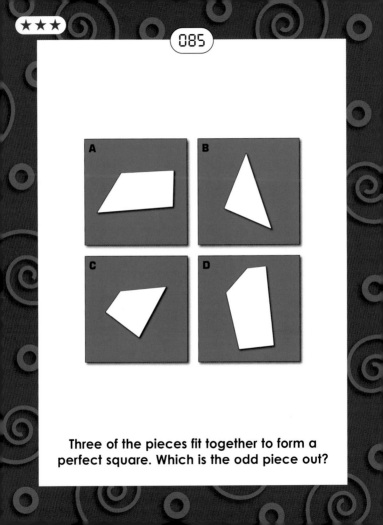

A

B

C

D

Three of the pieces fit together to form a
perfect square. Which is the odd piece out?

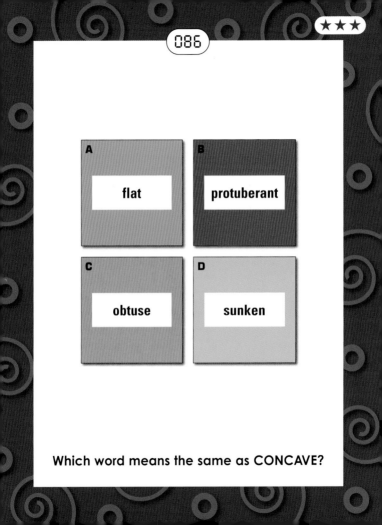

A

flat

B

protuberant

C

obtuse

D

sunken

Which word means the same as CONCAVE?

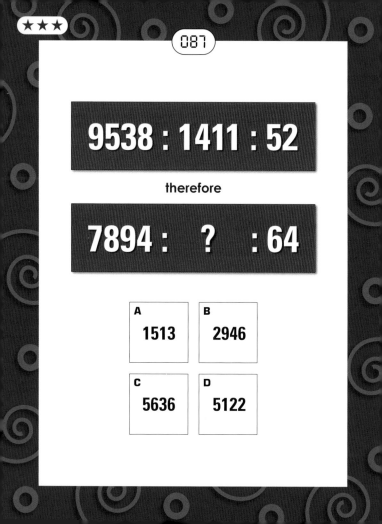

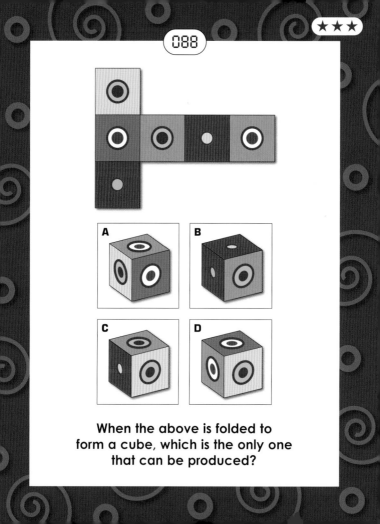

When the above is folded to form a cube, which is the only one that can be produced?

A **learned**

B **precise**

C **clever**

D **regular**

Which word means the
opposite of ERRONEOUS?

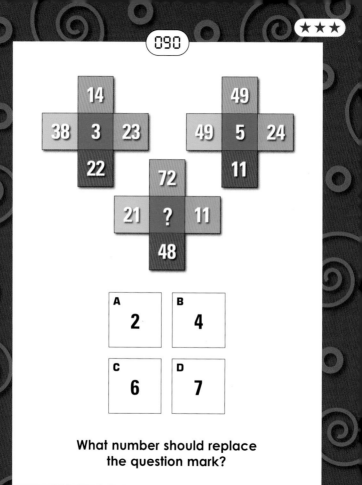

★★★

14
38 3 23
22

49
49 5 24
11

72
21 ? 11
48

A
2

B
4

C
6

D
7

What number should replace
the question mark?

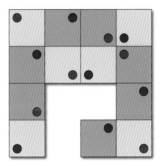

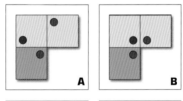

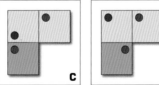

Which is the missing section?

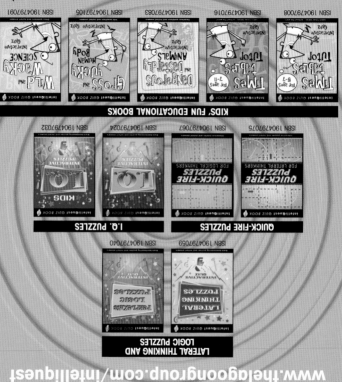

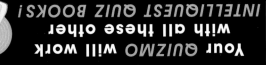

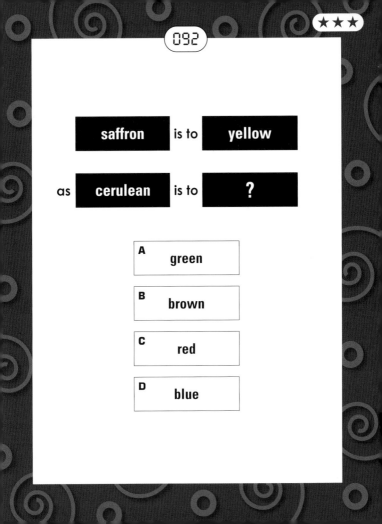

1, 3, 8, 16, 27, ?

A 41

B 39

C 47

D 43

What comes next?

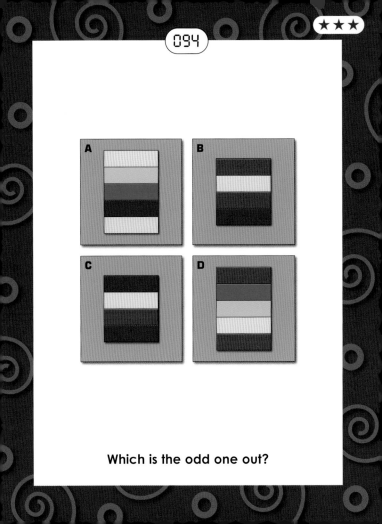

Which is the odd one out?

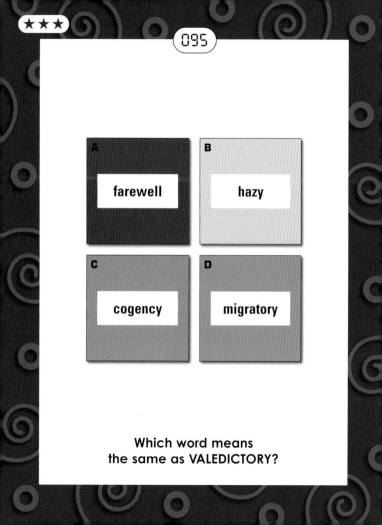

A

farewell

B

hazy

C

cogency

D

migratory

Which word means
the same as VALEDICTORY?

5	7	2	3
2	1	5	?
4	4	3	1
3	3	4	4
6	3	2	2

A 3

B 4

C 5

D 6

What number should replace
the question mark?

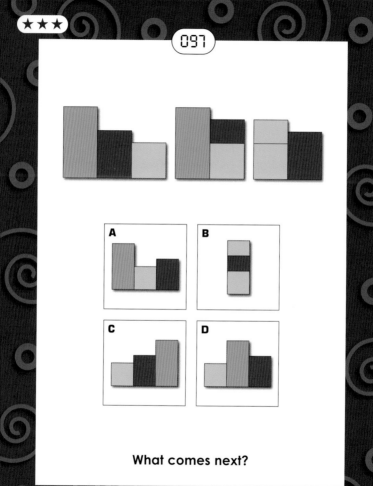

What comes next?

★★★

100, 98.5, 95.5, 91, 85, ?

A 77.5

B 78.5

C 77

D 76.5

What comes next?

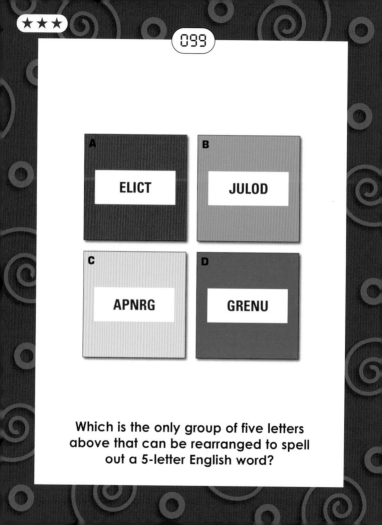

A

ELICT

B

JULOD

C

APNRG

D

GRENU

Which is the only group of five letters above that can be rearranged to spell out a 5-letter English word?

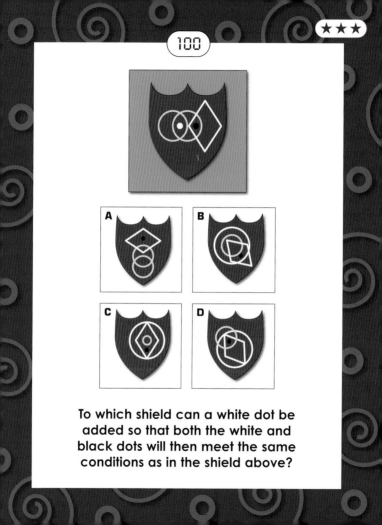

To which shield can a white dot be added so that both the white and black dots will then meet the same conditions as in the shield above?

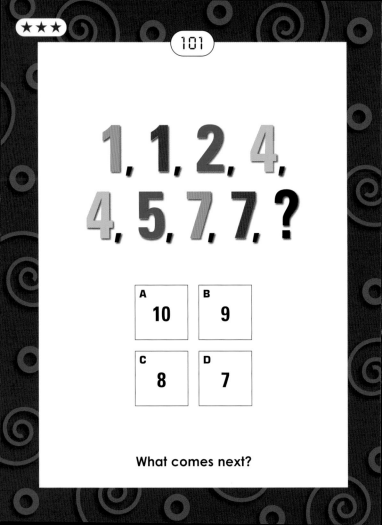

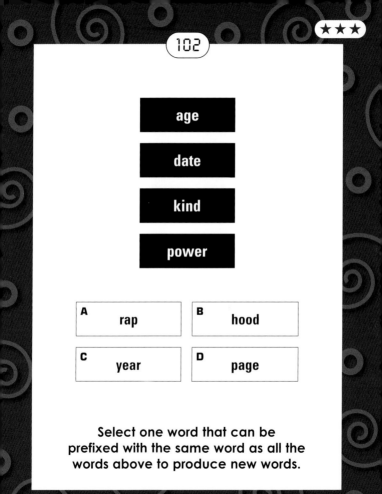

age

date

kind

power

A rap

B hood

C year

D page

Select one word that can be
prefixed with the same word as all the
words above to produce new words.

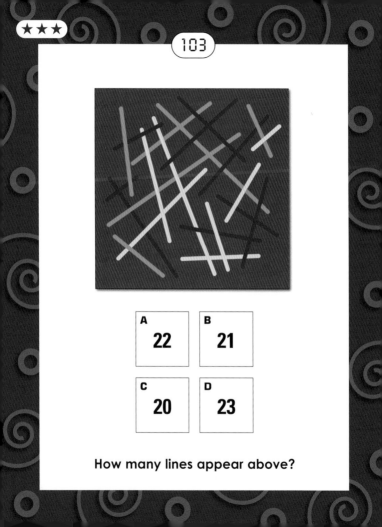

A
22

B
21

C
20

D
23

How many lines appear above?

A colt

B doe

C mare

D hind

Which is the odd one out?

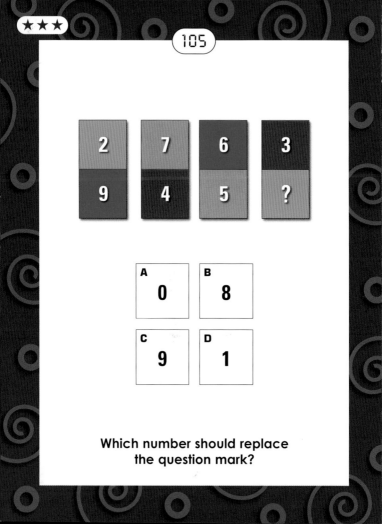

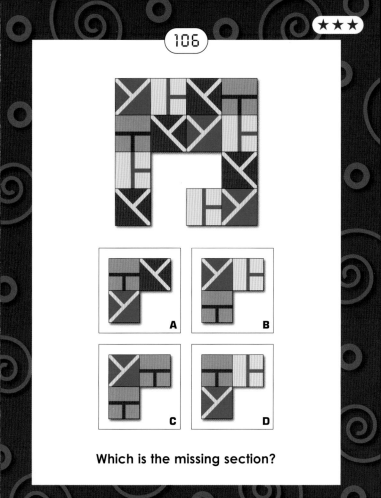

Which is the missing section?

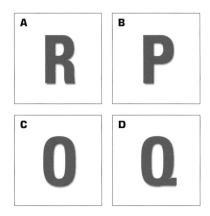

AZCXFUJ?

A	B
R	P

C	D
O	Q

What comes next?

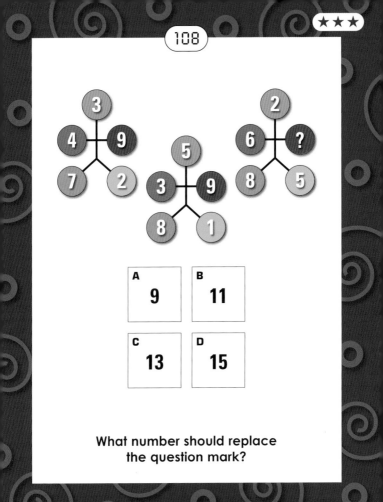

108

A 9

B 11

C 13

D 15

What number should replace
the question mark?

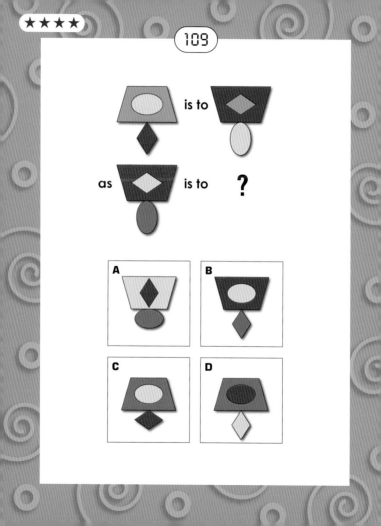

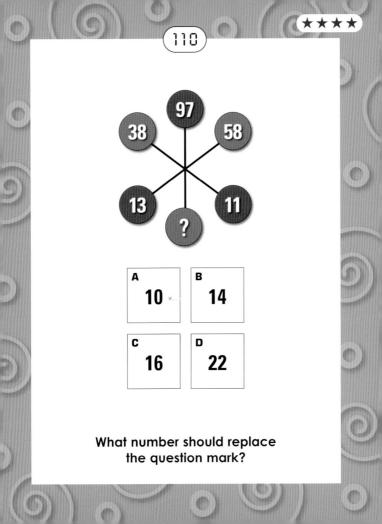

A 10

B 14

C 16

D 22

What number should replace
the question mark?

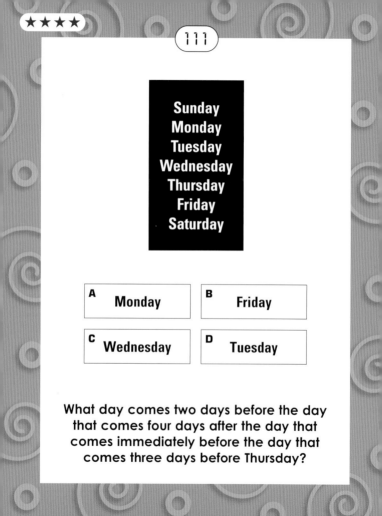

Sunday
Monday
Tuesday
Wednesday
Thursday
Friday
Saturday

A Monday

B Friday

C Wednesday

D Tuesday

What day comes two days before the day
that comes four days after the day that
comes immediately before the day that
comes three days before Thursday?

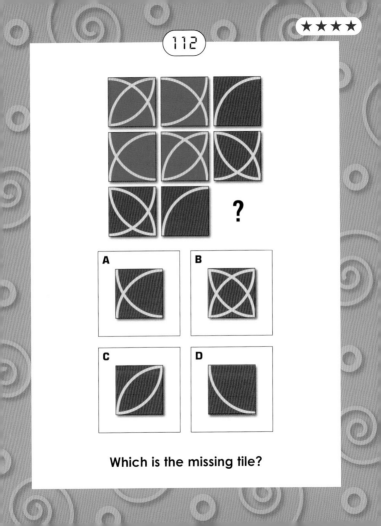

★★★★

A

B

C

D

?

Which is the missing tile?

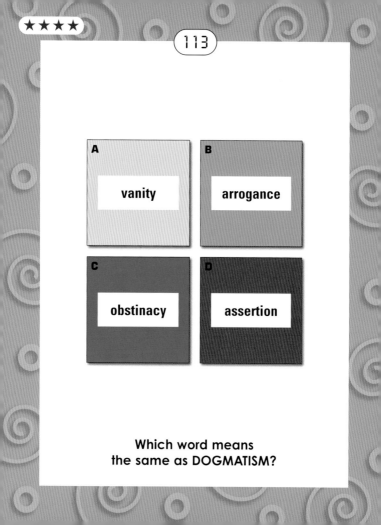

A vanity

B arrogance

C obstinacy

D assertion

Which word means
the same as DOGMATISM?

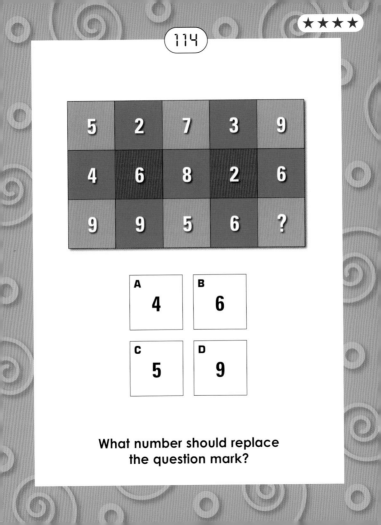

What number should replace
the question mark?

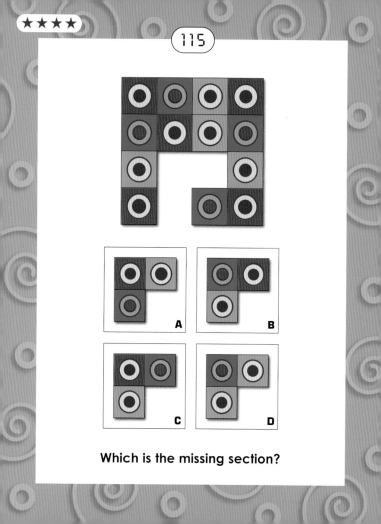

Which is the missing section?

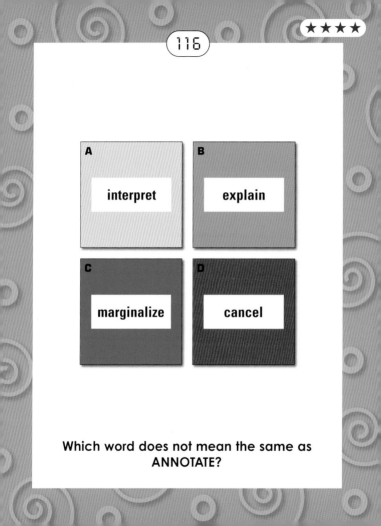

★★★★

A interpret

B explain

C marginalize

D cancel

Which word does not mean the same as
ANNOTATE?

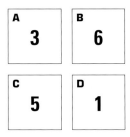

A 3

B 6

C 5

D 1

What number should replace
the question mark?

A

B

C

D

When the above is folded to
form a cube, which is the only one
that cannot be produced?

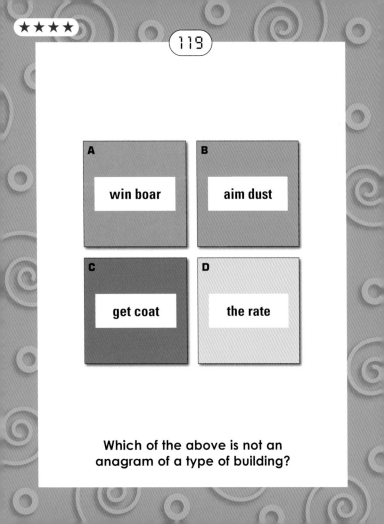

A

win boar

B

aim dust

C

get coat

D

the rate

Which of the above is not an
anagram of a type of building?

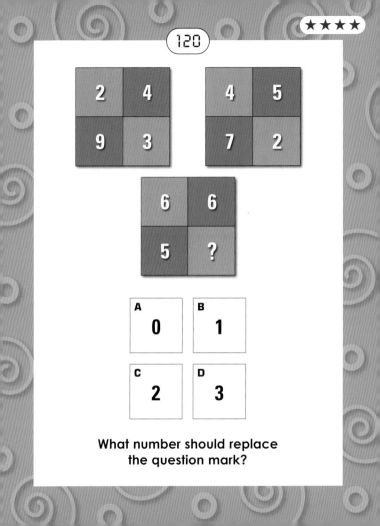

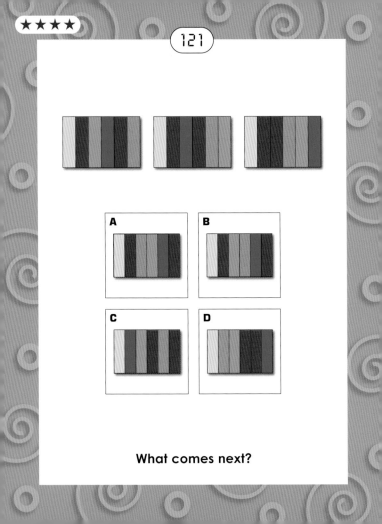

What comes next?

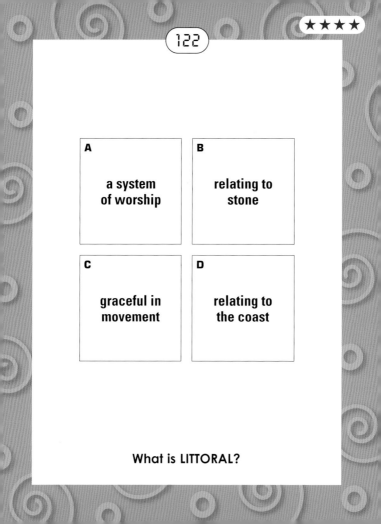

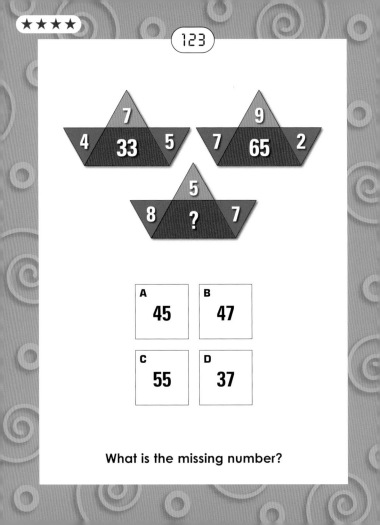

What is the missing number?

Which is the missing section?

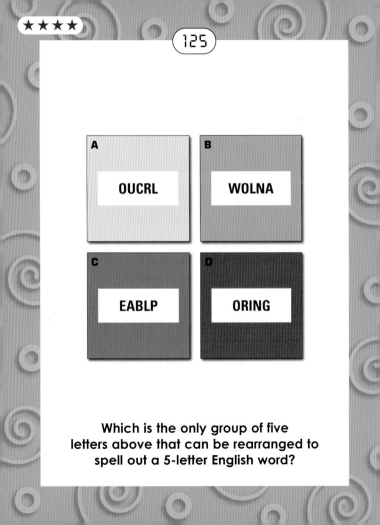

★★★★

125

A OUCRL

B WOLNA

C EABLP

D ORING

Which is the only group of five
letters above that can be rearranged to
spell out a 5-letter English word?

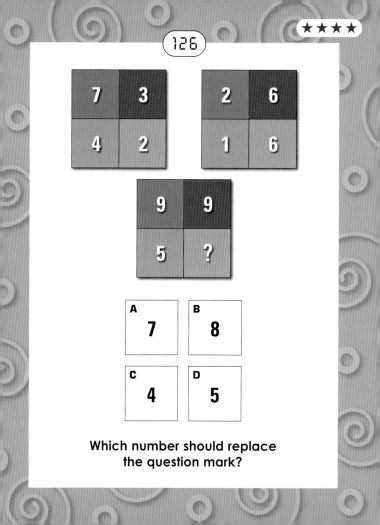

★ ★ ★ ★

| 7 | 3 |
| 4 | 2 |

| 2 | 6 |
| 1 | 6 |

| 9 | 9 |
| 5 | ? |

A 7

B 8

C 4

D 5

Which number should replace
the question mark?

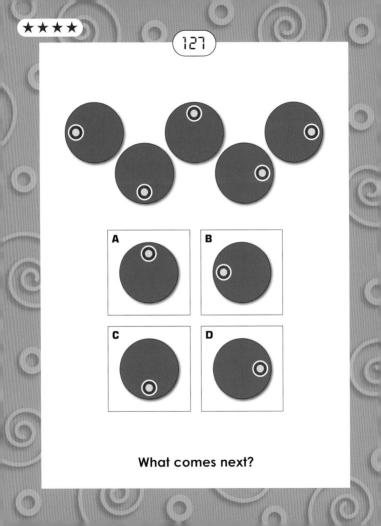

What comes next?

★★★★

A persiflage

B discourse

C banter

D badinage

Which is the odd one out?

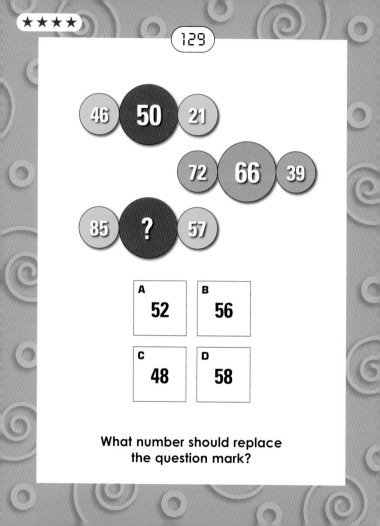

46 50 21

72 66 39

85 ? 57

A 52

B 56

C 48

D 58

What number should replace
the question mark?

Which is the odd one out?

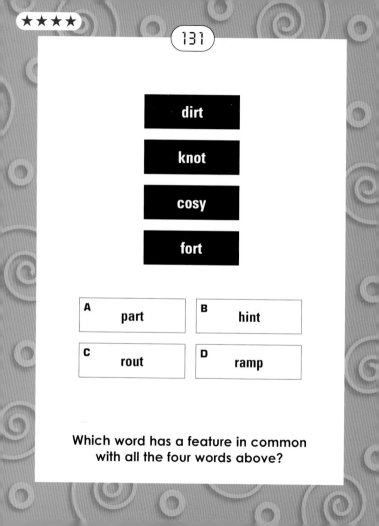

dirt

knot

cosy

fort

A part

B hint

C rout

D ramp

Which word has a feature in common
with all the four words above?

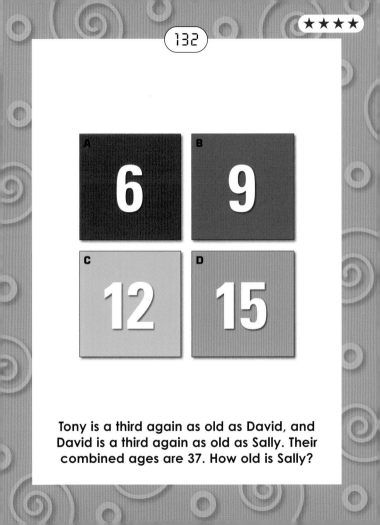

A 6

B 9

C 12

D 15

Tony is a third again as old as David, and David is a third again as old as Sally. Their combined ages are 37. How old is Sally?

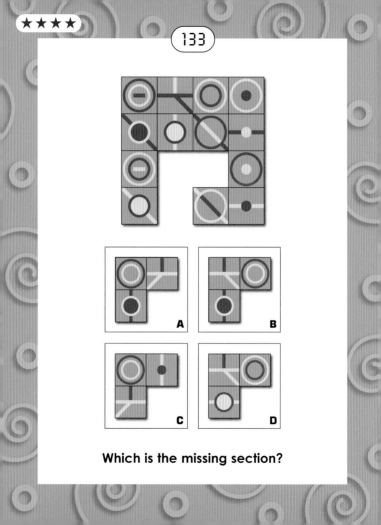

Which is the missing section?

A shrill

B decrepit

C nauseous

D carouse

Which word means
the same as SQUEAMISH?

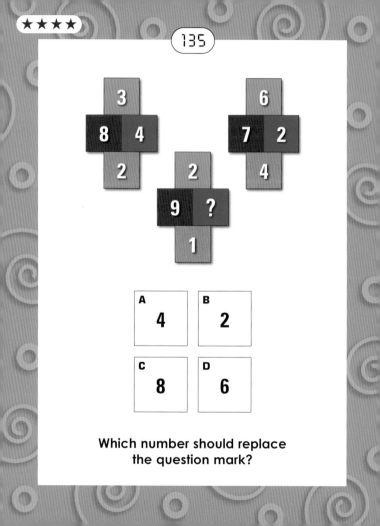

A 4

B 2

C 8

D 6

Which number should replace
the question mark?

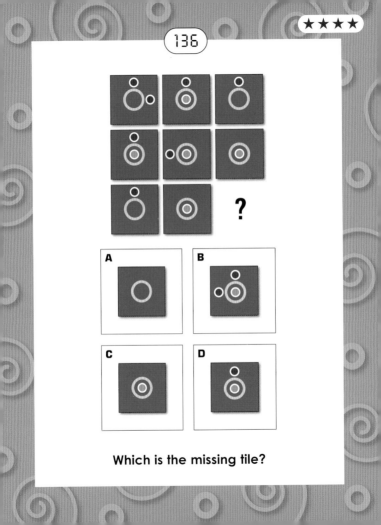

Which is the missing tile?

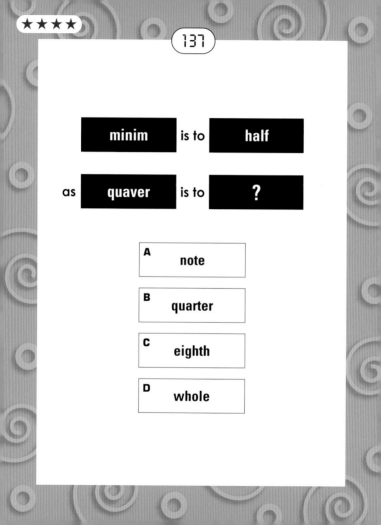

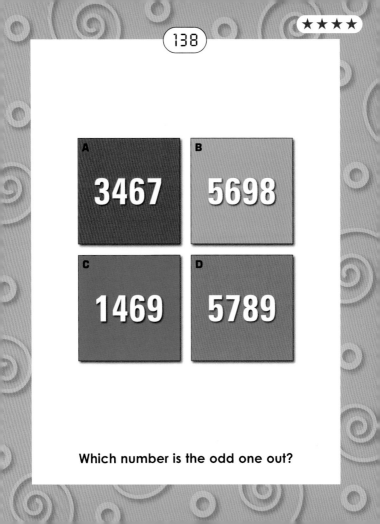

A 3467

B 5698

C 1469

D 5789

Which number is the odd one out?

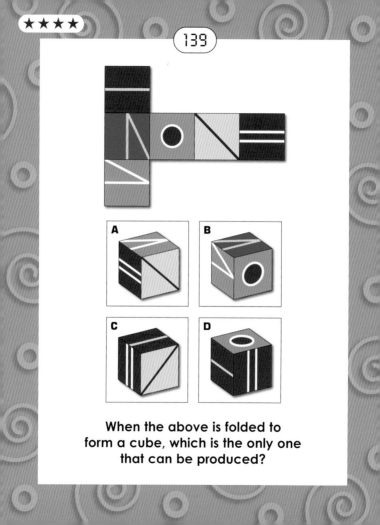

When the above is folded to
form a cube, which is the only one
that can be produced?

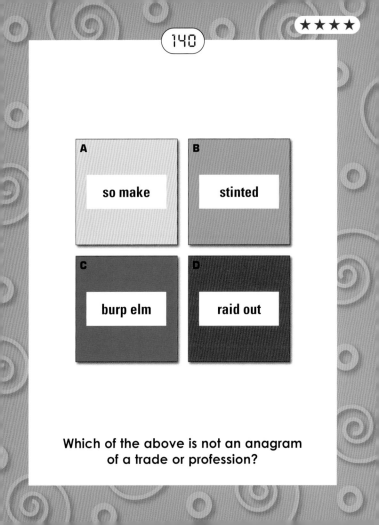

★ ★ ★ ★

140

A

so make

B

stinted

C

burp elm

D

raid out

Which of the above is not an anagram
of a trade or profession?

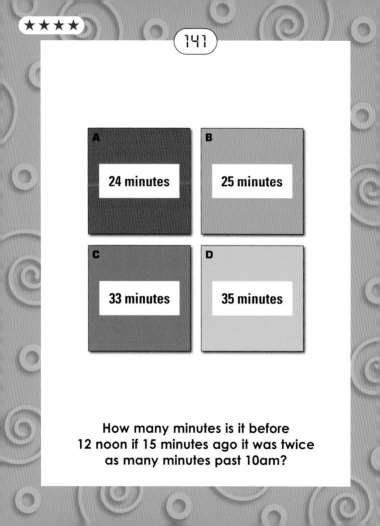

A 24 minutes

B 25 minutes

C 33 minutes

D 35 minutes

How many minutes is it before
12 noon if 15 minutes ago it was twice
as many minutes past 10am?

Which is the missing section?

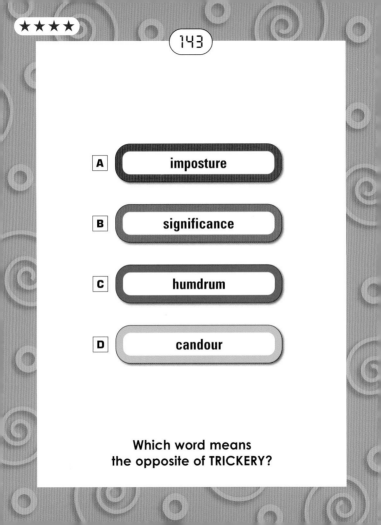

A   imposture

B   significance

C   humdrum

D   candour

Which word means
the opposite of TRICKERY?

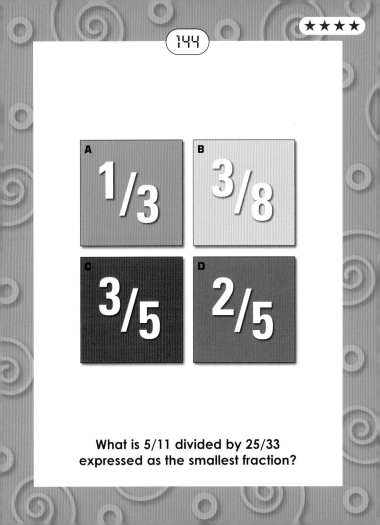

★ ★ ★ ★

A 1/3

B 3/8

C 3/5

D 2/5

What is 5/11 divided by 25/33
expressed as the smallest fraction?

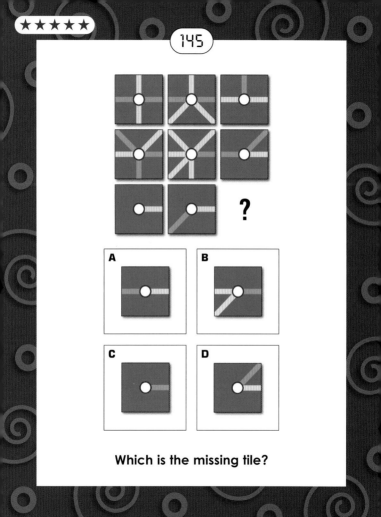

?

A

B

C

D

Which is the missing tile?

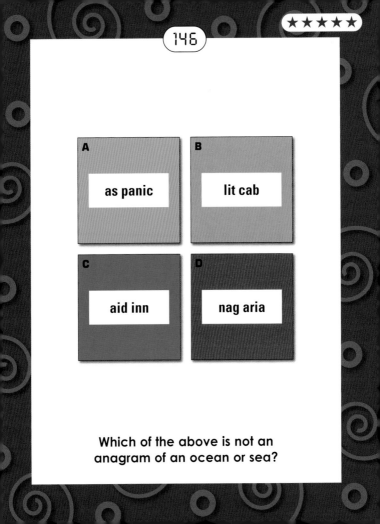

A as panic

B lit cab

C aid inn

D nag aria

Which of the above is not an
anagram of an ocean or sea?

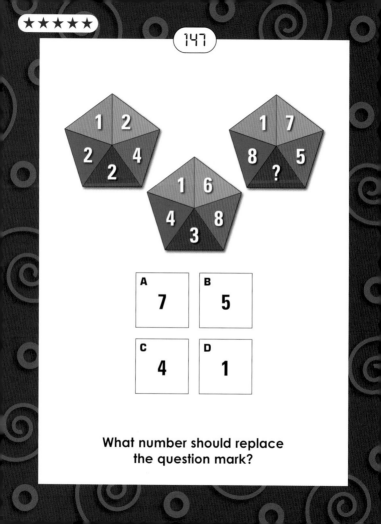

A
7

B
5

C
4

D
1

What number should replace
the question mark?

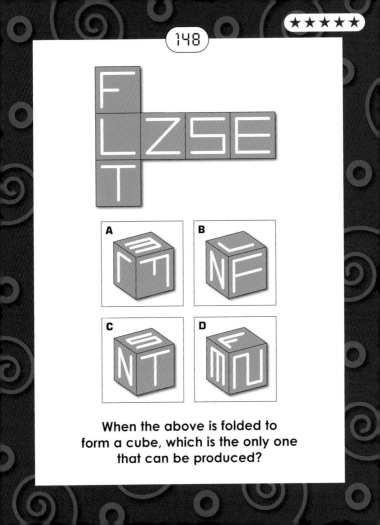

When the above is folded to form a cube, which is the only one that can be produced?

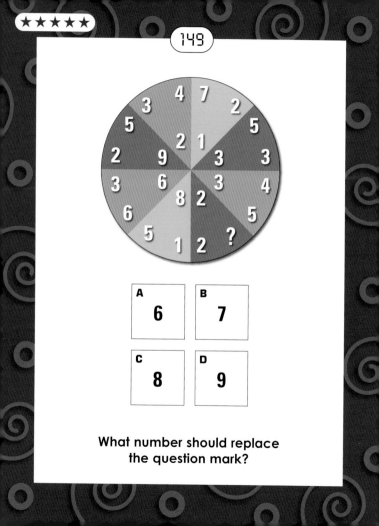

A 6

B 7

C 8

D 9

What number should replace
the question mark?

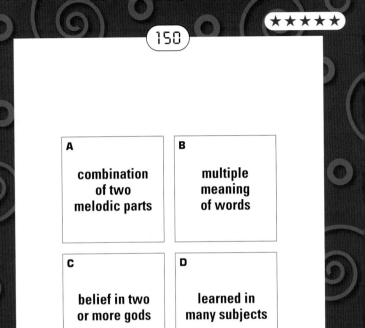

A

combination
of two
melodic parts

B

multiple
meaning
of words

C

belief in two
or more gods

D

learned in
many subjects

What is POLYSEMY?

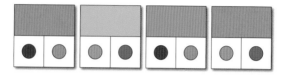

A

B

C

D

What comes next?

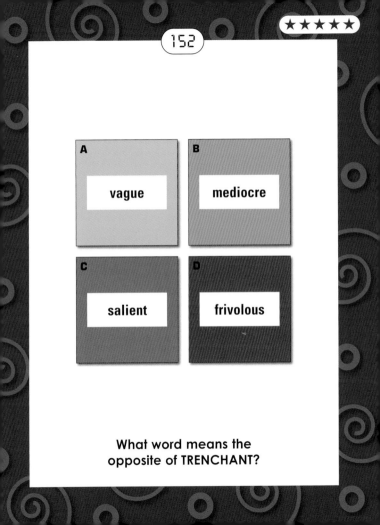

A vague

B mediocre

C salient

D frivolous

What word means the
opposite of TRENCHANT?

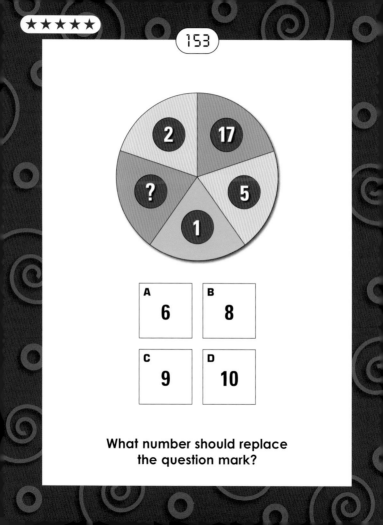

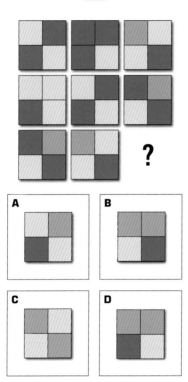

A

B

C

D

Which is the missing tile?

A **calcify**

B **change**

C **inveigle**

D **confuse**

Which word means the same as PETRIFY?

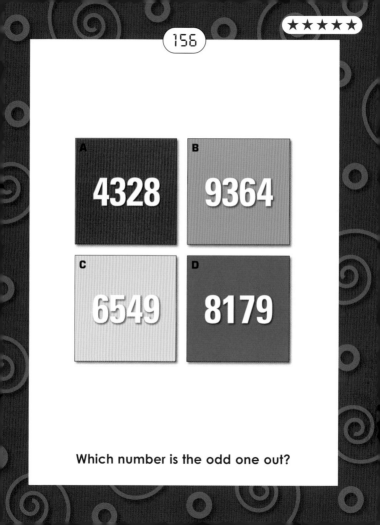

★★★★★

A 4328

B 9364

C 6549

D 8179

Which number is the odd one out?

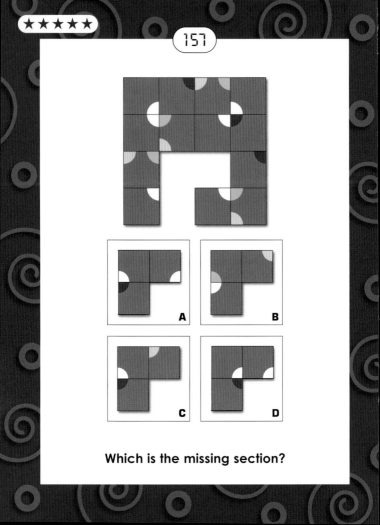

Which is the missing section?

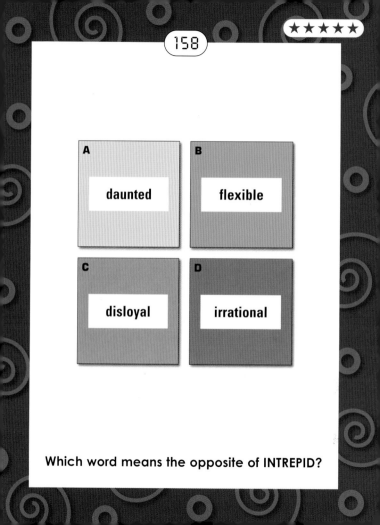

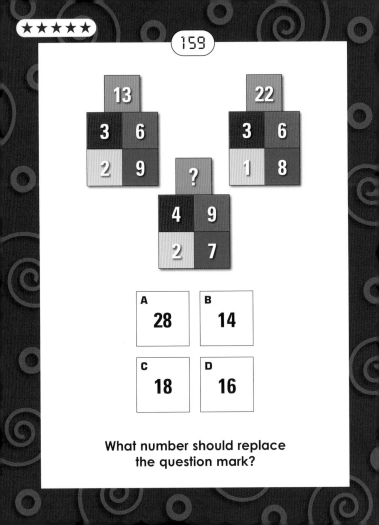

13

3 6

2 9

22

3 6

1 8

?

4 9

2 7

A
28

B
14

C
18

D
16

What number should replace
the question mark?

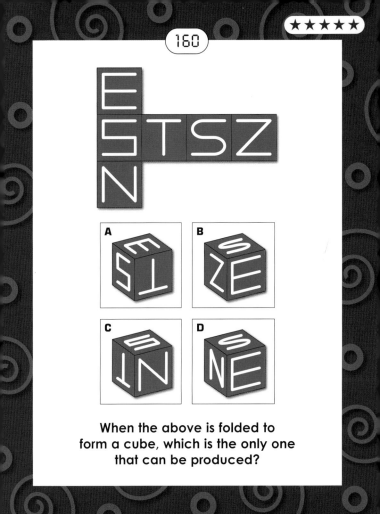

When the above is folded to
form a cube, which is the only one
that can be produced?

pascal is to **pressure**

as **kelvin** is to **?**

A   heat

B   frequency

C   temperature

D   speed

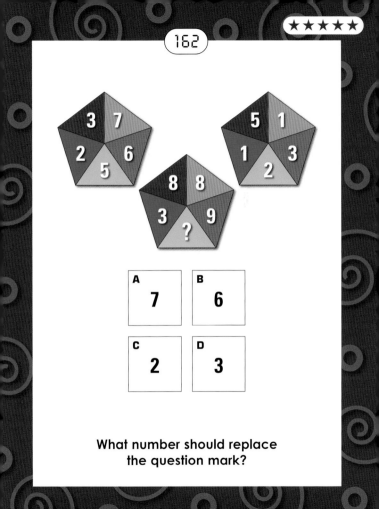

162

★ ★ ★ ★ ★

A 7

B 6

C 2

D 3

What number should replace
the question mark?

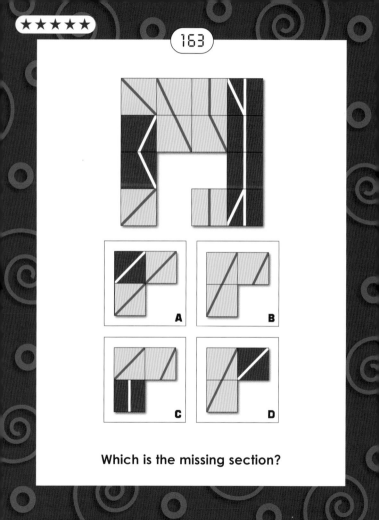

Which is the missing section?

★★★★★

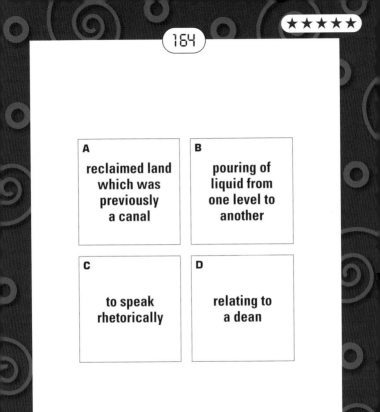

A

reclaimed land
which was
previously
a canal

B

pouring of
liquid from
one level to
another

C

to speak
rhetorically

D

relating to
a dean

What is the meaning of DECANAL?

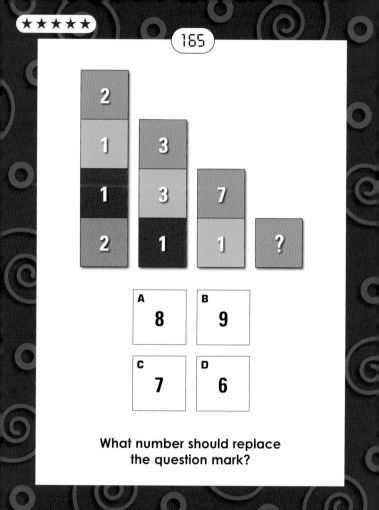

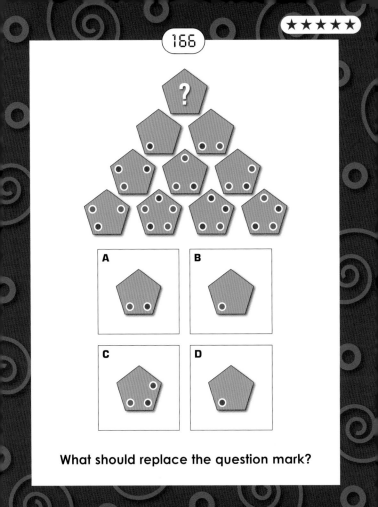

166

What should replace the question mark?

A

B

C

D

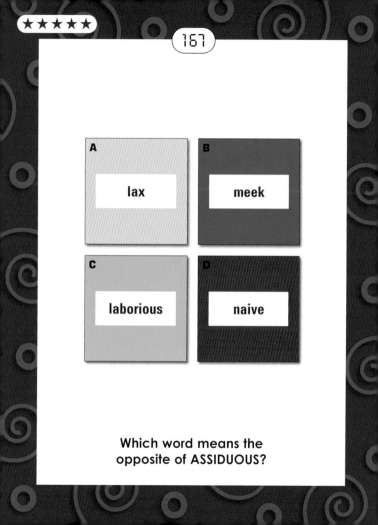

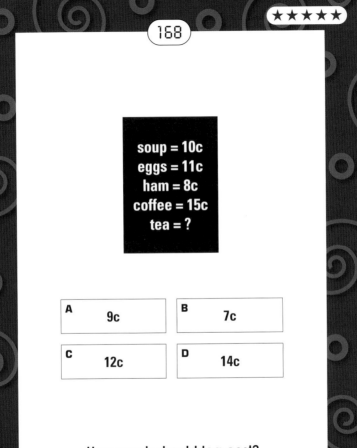

soup = 10c
eggs = 11c
ham = 8c
coffee = 15c
tea = ?

A 9c

B 7c

C 12c

D 14c

How much should tea cost?

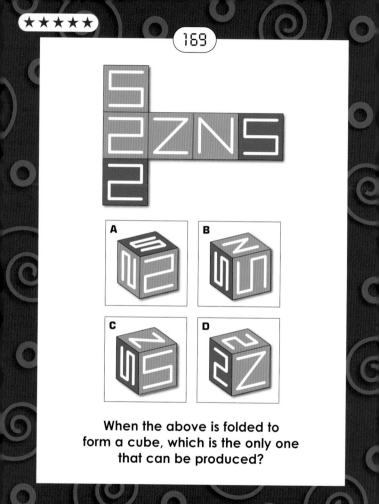

★★★★★

When the above is folded to
form a cube, which is the only one
that can be produced?

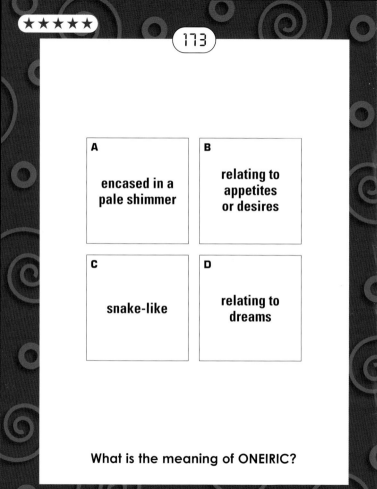

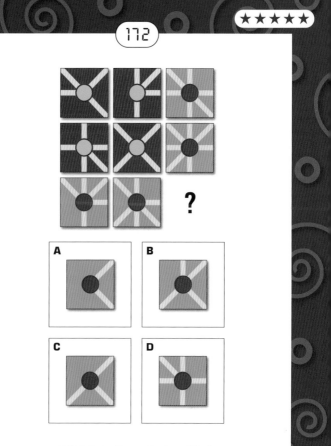

Which is the missing tile?

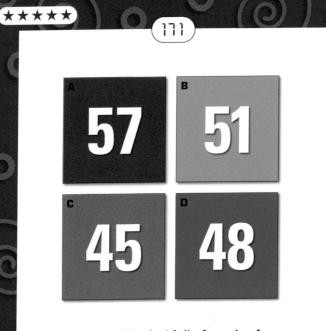

A 57

B 51

C 45

D 48

I picked a basket full of apples from my orchard. On my way home I met my son and gave him a third. I then ate two of the apples that were left and then gave two thirds of the remainder to my neighbour before arriving home with just ten apples. How many apples did I originally pick from my orchard?

A to plea

B hear cry

C hold pin

D all babes

Which of the above is not an
anagram of a game or sport?

174

★★★★★

8 9 2 6 3 8 9
3 6 2 9 8 3 6
9 2 6 3 8 9 2
8 3 _ _ 9 8 3
2 6 _ _ 9 2 6
9 8 3 6 2 9 8
6 3 8 9 2 6 3

A

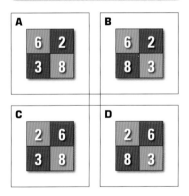

6 2 / 3 8

B

6 2 / 8 3

C

2 6 / 3 8

D

2 6 / 8 3

Which is the missing section?

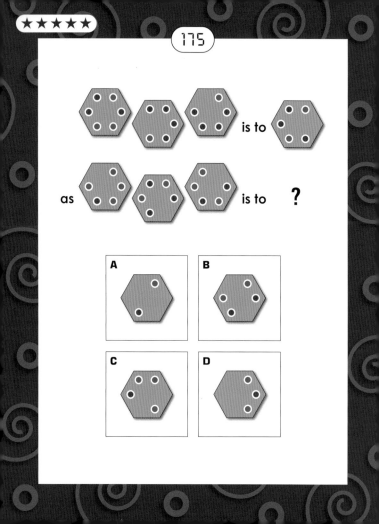

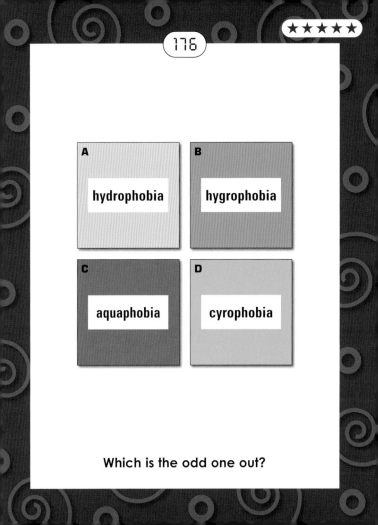

A hydrophobia

B hygrophobia

C aquaphobia

D cyrophobia

Which is the odd one out?

2, 4, 6, 12, 22, 40, 74, 138, ?

A 200

B 225

C 250

D 275

What comes next?

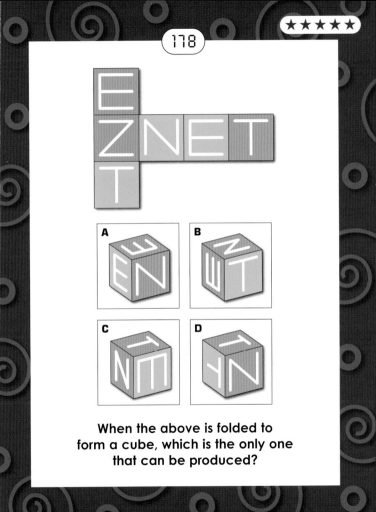

When the above is folded to
form a cube, which is the only one
that can be produced?

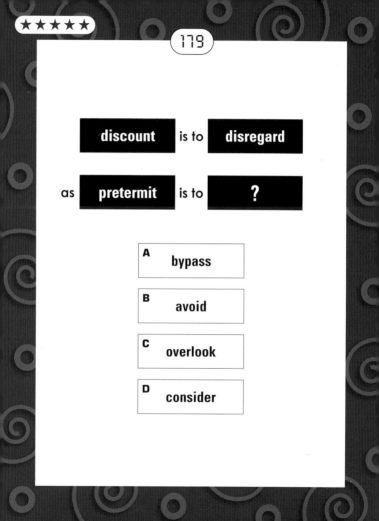

discount is to disregard

as pretermit is to ?

A bypass

B avoid

C overlook

D consider

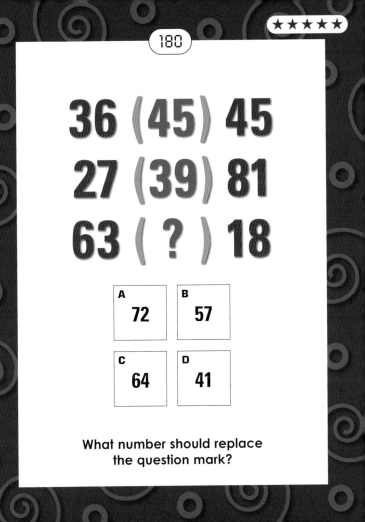

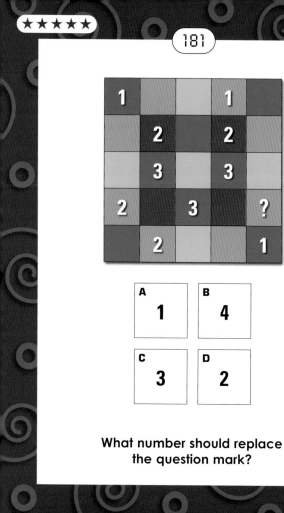

A
1

B
4

C
3

D
2

What number should replace
the question mark?

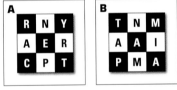

Which box should join these other two?

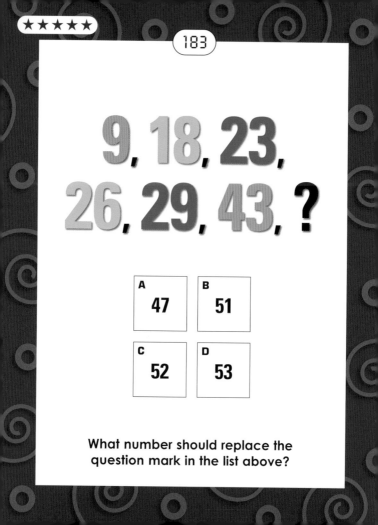

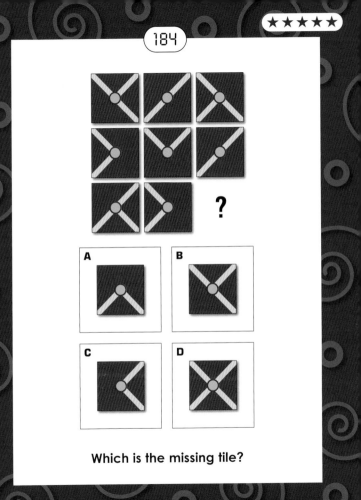

Which is the missing tile?

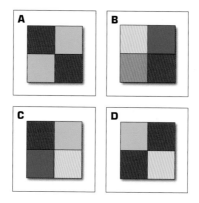

Which box should continue the sequence?

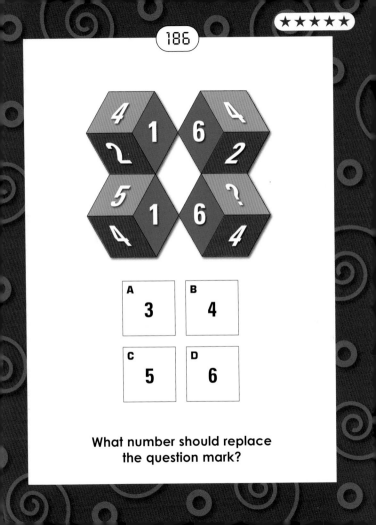

What number should replace
the question mark?